We hope you enjoy this book.
Please return or renew it by the due date.
You can renew it at **www.norfolk.gov.uk/libraries**
or by using our free library app. Otherwise you can
phone **0344 800 8020** - please have your library
card and pin ready.
You can sign up for email reminders too.

| | | |
|---|---|---|
| | | |

**NORFOLK COUNTY COUNCIL**
**LIBRARY AND INFORMATION SERVICE**

NORFOLK ITEM

3 0129 08435 8820

D0229461

# This CBeebies Annual belongs to

Published 2020.
Little Brother Books Limited, Ground Floor, 23 Southernhay East, Exeter, Devon EX1 1QL.
books@littlebrotherbooks.co.uk
The Little Brother Books Limited trademark, email and website are
the sole and exclusive properties of Little Brother Books Limited.

ISBN 978-1-912342-63-1

A CIP catalogue for this book is available from the British Library.

Content created by Immediate Media:
• Editor Hollie Mitchell • Deputy Editor Anna Burdal • Senior Writer Rebecca Lord • Writer/Sub Editor Gabrielle Meredith-Elsworth
• Senior Art Editor Anne-Marie Nosworthy • Art Editor Tania Rösler • Senior Designer Daisy Greenaway
• Joint Group Production Editors Marie-Louise Haig, Carolyn Parris
• Deputy Group Production Editor Will Demetriou • Production Editor Igrain Roberts

LB BOOKS

BBC

# Who's inside?

# Come on in!

Write and colour the CBeebies House song!

This is our house,

and it's so much fun.

Discover, make, move,

come on in, everyone!

Dance along too!

6

# All about me

## Tell the friends about yourself!

I'm Ben, nice to meet you!

My **name** is:

..........................................................................................

Draw a picture of yourself here!

I'm Rebecca. Great drawing!

Draw the number of candles you had at your last birthday!

Colour the cake.

My favourite animal is:

I'm Katy and I like tigers!

My favourite colour is:

9

# Number magic

Time for some number fun!

$$2 \quad + \quad 1 \quad =$$

$$4 \quad + \quad 1 \quad =$$

I've got 4 blocks!

10

10     −     2     =    ☐

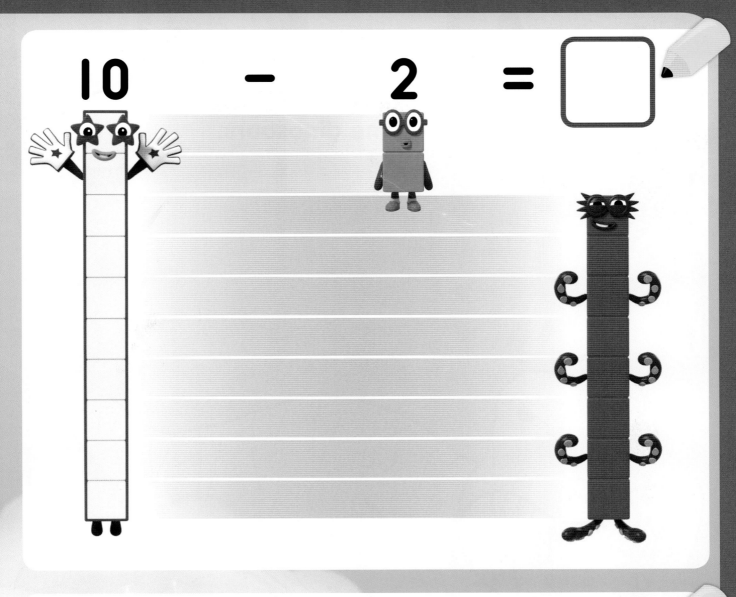

6     −     3     =    ☐

I am Three. Look at me!

# Adventure!

Colour and draw some roar-some dinosaurs.

ROAR!

Can you ROAR like a T-Rex?

roar

T-Rex had lots of teeth. Each tooth was as big as a banana!

Illustrations by: Ian Cunliffe.

# At the park

## Can you spot Waffle and friends?

What's that naughty dog doing now?

WOOF!

| Evie | Doug | Waffle | Simon | Jess | George |
|------|------|--------|-------|------|--------|
|  |  |  |  |  |  |
| ☐ | ☐ | ☐ | ☐ | ☐ | ☐ |

# Jokes!

## Laugh along with the Gigglebiz friends!

### Laugh-O-Meter

2 3 4
1 5

| Not funny at all. | Yawn, next joke! | Pretty giggly! | That's laugh out loud funny! | HAHAHA HAHAHA AHAHA! |

Colour each face to show how funny you found the joke!

**Why** should you be careful when it's raining cats and dogs?

Because you might step in a poodle!

woof!

**Why** was the footballer sad o his birthday?

Haway! Because he got a **red card!**

16

**Why** do wizards brush their teeth 10 times a day?

So they don't get bat breath!

**What** is a snake's favourite lesson?

Hisss-tory!

**What** did the sea say to the pirate?

Nothing, it just waved!

**Why** couldn't the teddy bear finish his cake?

Because he was stuffed!

# Puppet show

Round the corner, not far away,
Bing is doing a puppet show today!

**1**

Bing and Sula are putting on a **puppet show** for Flop, Pando and Amma. "We're stuck up a very big, high mountain," says Sula. "Biteysaurus, come and save us!" says Bing. "Fairy Hippo is coming in for landing!" giggles Sula. Just then, the doorbell rings.

**2**

It's Coco, Charlie and Doctor Molly. "Wow, a show! **Can I play?** My Rainbow Fairy Mouses* are very good at flying!" announces Coco. "Oh, okay, you sit on your bum-bum, Coco, and you can have a turn when this exciting show is finished," says Amma.

**3** "The Rainbow Fairy Mice can watch too," laughs Coco, as she lines them up on the rug. "Bulaballo and Hoppity can't see, Coco!" says Pando. **"Nobody's listening,"** notices Bing.

The show isn't finished yet!

**4** "Maybe they can't hear us, Bing. You have to be **loud** when you do a show!" giggles Sula. **"Oh, ok. RARRRRRR!"** roars Bing. "You are being rescued! Let's fly away!" laughs Sula and they race around the room. "Is it finished?" asks Coco. "Not yet!" says Bing, zooming back to the stage. "BITEYSAURUS HAS TO SAVE THE WHOLE WORLD! RARRRR!" roars Bing, really loudly, right into Sula's ear. **"Ouch! Not so loud, Bing,"** says Sula.

RARR!

**5** "You'll wake Charlie, Bing!" says Coco. "You said you have to be LOUD when you do a show," says Bing. **"But Biteysaurus is too loud and bitey, Bing. He's hurted\* my ears,"** says Sula.

**6** "But Biteysaurus is in the show," sighs Bing as he puts Biteysaurus on the floor and goes to sit on the bottom step by himself. Flop joins Bing at the bottom of the stairs with Biteysaurus. **"I want to go home, Flop. Biteysaurus is sad now,"** Bing says quietly. "He does look a bit sad," agrees Flop.

Biteysaurus is sad.

**7** Sula moves closer to Bing. "We could do a **new show,** Bing. With Biteysaurus! If he's a bit more... quiet?" suggests Sula. "Biteysaurus does want to be in the show. And he's **sorry for giving you hurty ears,"** says Bing. "That's ok, Bitey," smiles Sula.

20

Puppet Show, original story written by Helen Farrall, Mikael Shields and Claire Jennings. *These spellings are Bingisms.

**8** Just then, Bing has an idea. "I've got sore teeth now, from too much biting. And a sore throat now, from too much rarring," he whispers. **"Oh! Dr Fairy Hippo can help. She has special medicine for sore teeth!"** giggles Sula as they run back to the stage. "Whoosh! The Rainbow Fairy Mouses* will make his throat better too!" joins in Coco.

That was brilliant!

**9** "Thank you! I do feel better now," says Bing as Biteysaurus. **"Come on, Biteysaurus, Fairy Hippo and Rainbow Fairy Mouses*. Let's go and save the whole world!"** giggles Bing. When the puppet show is over, everybody takes a bow. "Best show ever!" cheers Pando!

Putting on a show... it's a Bing thing!

# Pirate moves!

## Get moving with the Swashbuckle crew.

Colour a star when you've done the move!

Aharrr!

Do the Swashbuckle salute!

Mop the slop!

Move sideways like a crab!

SNIP!

SNAP!

Give a big pirate cheer!

## Do a star jump!

## Climb the rigging!

## Have a 10 second dance party!

# Picnic!

Draw different shapes to finish the picture.

Bibbleberry buns!

Tick if you drew these shapes.

circle

triangle

oval

rectangle

# Opposites

Solve some puzzles with Kit and Pup!

**Is Pup above or below the bridge?**

above | below

**Is Kit standing on something solid or in a liquid?**

liquid | solid

**Pup's suitcase is...**

open | closed

**Kit's bike is...**

long | short

26

# Colour!

Use your pencils to finish the picture.

# Clap your hands!

### Sing and sign with Mr Tumble.

If you're  **happy** and  **you**

If  **you're**  **happy** and  **you**

## Now try this verse...

If **you're happy** and **you know it, turn around!**

**turn around**

**colour**

## Colour Tumble Ted!

**sing**

**sign**

**know** it, **clap** your hands. x2

**know** it, and you really want to **show** it, If you're happy and you know it, clap your hands!

Tumble Ted is happy too!

Football
is fun
exercise!

31

# Oh, Waffle!

## Try these picture puzzles.

Waffle good dog!

✔ **What** do you think Waffle's fur feels like?

- [ ] fluffy
- [ ] hard
- [ ] prickly
- [ ] soft

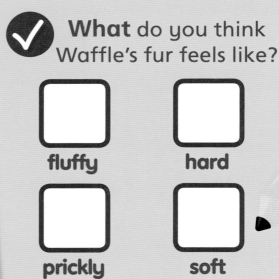

**Who** has Waffle painted a picture of?

**George**

**Mrs Hobbs**

**Trace** to see who Waffle is visiting.

miaow

It's George!

**Finish** the sentence.

**Waffle is**

sitting

**with his family.**

Did Waffle get stuck going **under** or **over** the fence?

Oh dear, Waffle!

**under**

**over**

Which **doggy friend** is in the picture?

**Baxter**

**Jelly**

# Let's bake!

Help Sarah and Duck make a cake.

Quack!

Swirl the mixture with your finger.

✓ **Can you spot these things?**

flour

baking powder

poppy seeds

**Draw a smiley face on this cake!**

We need to give it a good mix!

**Add colour to quacky Duck!**

**How do you think Duck is feeling?**
Circle a picture.

milk

**Happy Duck!**

**Sad Duck!**

35

OCTONAUTS

# Arctic mission

**Find out about two cold creatures!**

## walrus

These friends are found in shallow waters and on ice.

whiskers

Walruses use their sensitive **whiskers** to find things on the sea floor.

Walruses can **say hello** by blowing air into each other's faces.

tusks

They sometimes use these to fight each other!

flippers

Walruses will show they're in charge by slapping their **flippers** together.

A narwhal's tusk is actually **a giant tooth!**

**Draw** around the tusk.

Narwhals live in groups called **pods.**

**Colour** some narwhal friends.

They're the only whales to **travel through and under ice!**

They're sometimes called the unicorns of the sea!

We use our tusks to find our way!

# narwhal

Good work me'hearties!

# Mix it up!

## Let's learn about making new colours.

 If you mix 2 colours, you get a new one!

**red** + **yellow** = **orange**

**yellow** + **blue** = **green**

**blue** + **red** = **purple**

**Now** colour these carrots and pumpkins **red**, then add **yellow** over the top to make **orange**!

 Lovely!

38

# Silly squiggles

### Turn the friends into giggly doodles.

**You could doodle:**

a fluttery butterfly

a tall sunflower

a bumbly beetle

a buzzy bee

Do we look funny, Lola?

We look absolutely giggly!

39

# Number race

## Find a friend for this counting game!

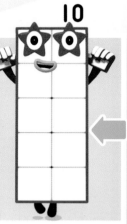

**10**

**FINISH!**

**5**

Give yourself a high five!

Write your favourite number here!

**Stand** on **1** leg for **10** seconds.

Do **1** star jump.

**Count** the butterflies.

Nod **3** times.

**Count up** to your age and roll again!

**Roll** an odd number to move on.

Clap **10** times.

**START**

**Clap 1** time.

Count the hats.

I'm odd!

**3**

**Roll** an odd number to move on.

**40**

**6**

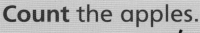
Find a dice and let's play!

**1** Choose a counter for each player. Put them on the START arrow.

**2** Take turns rolling a dice and moving along the board.

**3** When you land on a space, follow the instruction.

**4** The first player to reach the FINISH is the winner!

**Count** the apples.

**Hop** on 1 leg **8** times.

**8**

**Count** the colours.

**Count** the drinks.

**Trace** the number.

**5**

Roll an even number to move on.

**2**

**Trace** the number.

**9**

**Count** up to **8**.

**Stand** on 1 leg for 7 seconds.

**7**

**Roll** an even number to move on.

I'm even!

**4**

**Clap 5** times.

**Trace** the number.

**6**

# Cat!

Draw, colour and write to learn a new word with Dee.

Cat! Chasing cat!

**Trace** the trail.

**Write** the word.

cat

**Colour** the cat basket.

sleepy **cat**

Purrr!

Purr!

cool **cat**

Cat! You say cat.

42

# Coding!

**Follow the steps to reach the finish.**

Coding is the name for the instructions that tell computers what to do!

**Start**

**Finish**

1. Put your pencil on **start**.

2. Move **2 squares** to the right.

3. Now move **down 2 squares**.

4. Move **1 square** to the right.

5. Move **down 2 squares to finish**. You made it!

Can you **make up your own instructions** to get to the end a different way?

That was fun!

43

# In the garden

Add lots of colour to the Furchesters!

COOKIE!

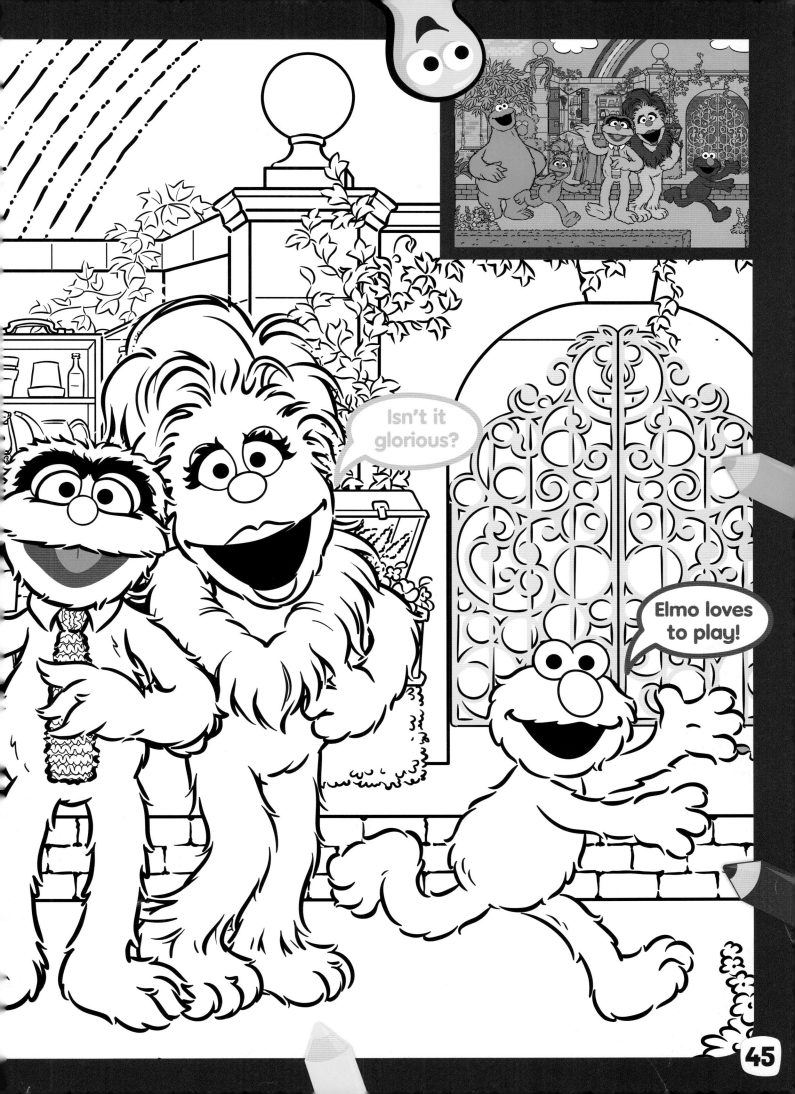

# Word fun

## Circle and write to solve the puzzles!

| j | b | b | m |
|---|---|---|---|
| a | w | u | i |
| m | n | n | l |
| e | g | g | k |

jam

egg

bun

milk

Try this tasty wordsearch!

# Solving fun

Try these funny puzzles!

## Circle the Duggee who comes next.

## Draw lines to match the close-up pictures to the right Duggees.

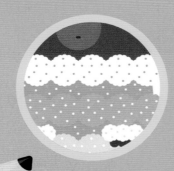

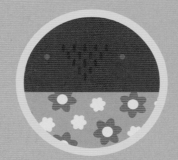

How many **red** fish can you spot?

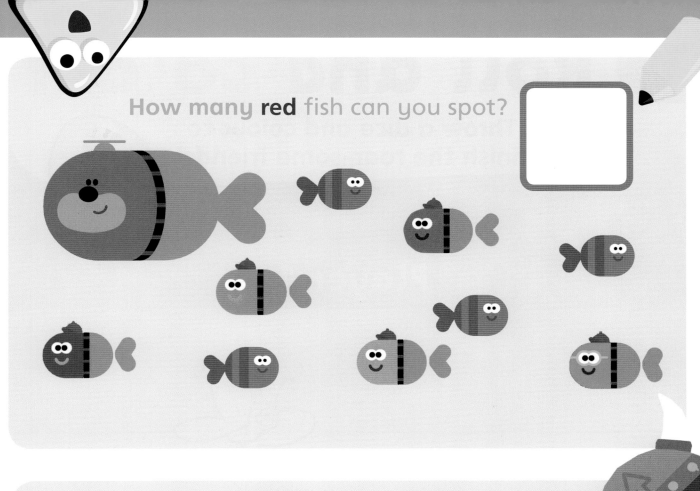

**Finish** the sentences.

Roly's smelly sock is

green

STINKY!

Colour the star green.

Happy's workout vest is

purple

Colour the star purple.

# Roll and colour

### Throw a dice and colour to finish the roar-some friends!

## Player 1

1

2

3

4

5

6

1 **Choose** who will be player 1 and who will be player 2. Take turns **rolling** a **dice**. **Colour** the same section as the number you roll!

2 You need to **roll all 6 numbers** to finish your picture. The first player to finish is the **winner!**

# Player 2

1

2

3

4

5

6

51

# Lynx and lion

## Find out about these big cats!

A lynx is a great hunter. It can see and hear really well!

## Warm coat

A lynx's **golden** or spotty fur grows thicker in winter to keep it warm.

## Big paws

Wide, **padded paws** make it brilliant at walking on **snow!**

## Shhh!

It can move very **quietly.**

Can you tell which is the lynx's fur?

**Draw** around the **snowy prints.**

lion

## Mane
Can you see the **long hair** around his head? Only **male lions** have this and **it's** called a mane.

## Roar
A lion's **roar** can be heard **from far** away!

ROAR!

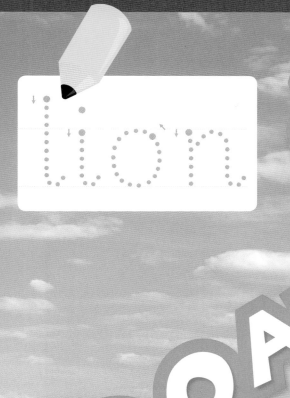

## Fast
Lions can run **really fast** on their **strong legs**.

A female lion is called a lioness!

**Circle** the **male** lion.

# Space maze

## Go on a space adventure with the bugs!

START

Hello!

Bleugh!

Wiggle, wiggle!

How many green aliens?

How many red aliens?

Grrr!

Bloop!

FINISH

How many
space bugs?

55

# Check-up!

## Help Ferne and Rory look after these pets.

### PUPPY

This puppy might be hot as it is panting...

**39°c**

woof!

...**Colour** the thermometer to check his temperature.

**Dogs** need lots of care and attention.

**Colour** some food and water too.

### budgie

tweet tweet

**Colour** the droplets to give the bird a bath.

**Budgies** like to live in groups so they shouldn't be alone!

Trace to wrap the wing in a bandage.

## kitten

Tick to show this is a healthy kitten.

 ✓ **fluffy fur**

 ✓ **no fleas**

 ✓ **bright eyes**

**Kittens** need lots of toys to play with.

*miaow!*

**Use** your fingers to brush the fur!

## rabbit

**Circle** what is needed to check this rabbit's heartbeat.

**stethoscope**    **carrot**

**Rabbits** need food, water and new bedding every day!

2kg   3kg
1kg   4kg
0     5kg

**How much** does this rabbit weigh?

.............. **kg**

Rabbits like to be kept in pairs as they enjoy company!

# Where's Duggee?

**HEY DUGGEE**

**Who else can you spot in the jungle?**

**Count** how many animals you can spot and write the number in each box.

cheeky monkeys

3

bouncy bunnies

4

clucky chickens

7

HELLO, EVERYONE!

# Spot the changes!

Colour a number when you see a difference.

1 2 3 4 5

There are 10 to spot!

**Which vehicles** are in the pictures?

Vroomster

Grimbler

Zoomster

Truckster

Add up all the Grimbots you can see. **How many** are there in total?

6 7 8 9 10

Ace job, cadet!

61

# Emergency!

## Write to label these amazing machines.

airport fire engine

hose

This **pumps water** to put out fires.

This huge machine can put out fires at the airport!

wheels

They're **very big** so they can go over grass as well as roads!

Emergency vehicles are **brightly** coloured so they can be easily spotted.

Which machine is needed...

...to put out fires at an airport?

☑

or

airport fire engine

ambulance

...to get someone to hospital quickly?

☑

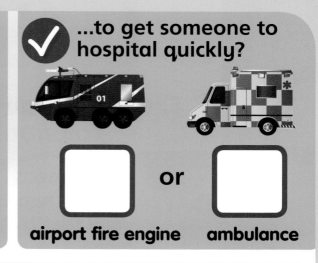

or

airport fire engine

ambulance

# ambulance

siren

It's **very noisy** to let people know the ambulance is coming through!

nee naw!

AMBULANCE

Ambulances get people to the hospital really quickly!

They **flash** to get other people's attention!

lights

Emergency vehicles move **super quickly** so they can help save people's lives!

slow   pretty fast   fast   super speedy

Draw an arrow to show their speed.

# Let's play

Find out all about drumming with YolanDa and Talbert.

Drummers use their hands and feet to make a beat.

## Clap out rhythms using animal words!

1 clap: **dog**

2 claps: **don-key**

3 claps: **el-eph-ant**

4 claps: **all-ig-at-or**

Now write your name and clap out the rhythm.

............................................................................................

64

# Make shakers!

Drums are percussion instruments! Percussion is anything you can hit, scrape or shake!

Pop some **pasta** or **rice** in an empty **yogurt pot.**

**Tape** another yogurt pot on top!

**Decorate** with strips of card, and let's shake!

Shake!
Shake!

Shake!

## Try this too!

**Tap** your hands against your legs 4 times!

Now **pat** your hands against your cheeks 2 times.

Can you hear the **different sounds** they make?

65

# In space!

## What can Major Clanger see through his telescope?

# Stargazing

Join the dots to reveal the star pictures!

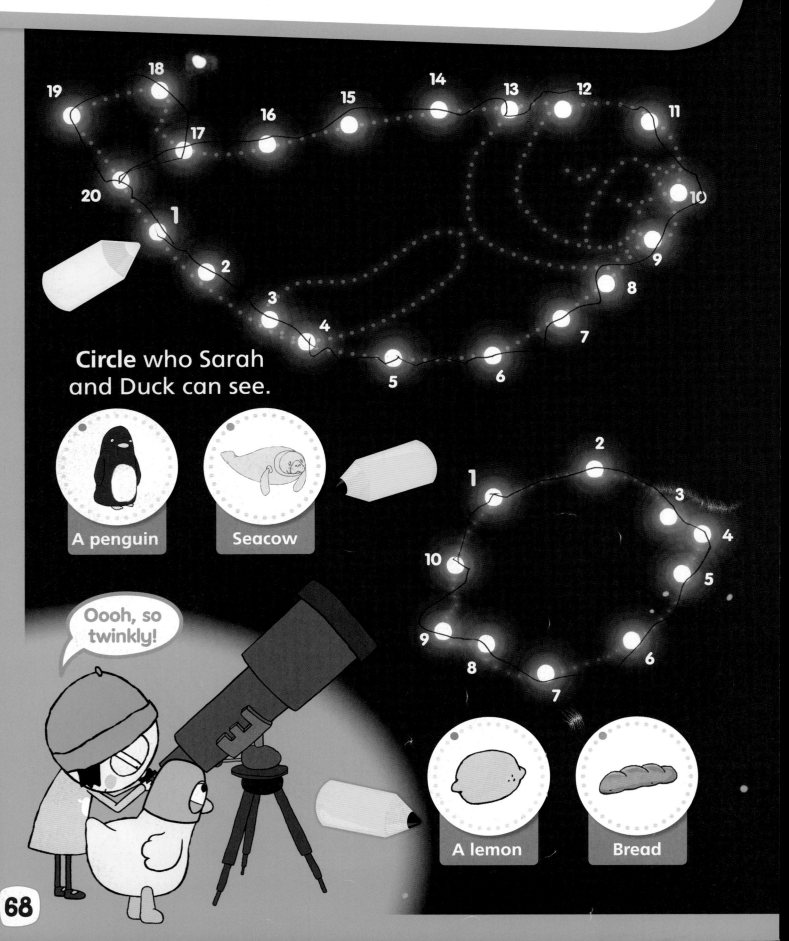

**Circle** who Sarah and Duck can see.

A penguin

Seacow

Oooh, so twinkly!

A lemon

Bread

68

Lovely evening we're having!

Scarf Lady

Bag

Donkey

Bug

You can try **stargazing** too!

✓ On a clear night, wrap up warm with a grown-up and look for these **star constellations**!

Tick if you spot them!

Quack!

**Ursa Major** (larger bear)

**Ursa Minor** (lesser bear)

# Bedtime book

## B can't sleep and needs a story!

**Try** sounding out these words before you start.

"I wish someone would tell me a bedtime story," said **B**. Suddenly, the other Alphablocks appeared. **O** and **K** had an idea. **O** split in two to make **OO**.

"**b - o o - k**  !" they said. A big **book** appeared in front of the Alphablocks. **OO** opened it and lots of letters fell out. "Oo!" said **OO**. "Once upon a time," started the **book** ,

"there was a girl called Little Red Riding...?" Oh no! There was a word missing! OO held hands with H and D,

and said, "h-oo-d  !" "Little Red Riding Hood! Yes, you're right!" said the **book** .

"Little Red Riding **Hood** went to visit her grandma, who lived on the other side of a deep, dark...?" The book stopped again. This time, OO held hands with M and N.

"m-oo-n  !" they said.

"Don't you mean *wood*?" said the book. "No, we like **moon** ," said the Alphablocks.

The **book** tutted and carried on. "Just then, out jumped a big, bad...?" The book waited as the Alphablocks changed places again.

"**w-o o-f**  !" they giggled.

"But it's supposed to be wolf!" said the **book** .

"Huh, well the **woof** was very big and very...?"

The Alphablocks changed once more, held hands and said, "**g-o o-d** !"

The **book** sighed. "So the big **good** **woof** kept the girl safe as they walked to her grandmother's...?" The **book** stopped.

The Woof was called the Big Bad Woof because he was very big and very

So the Big Good Woof kept Little Red Riding Hood safe as they walked to her grandmother's **boot.**

The Alphablocks swapped around and said, " **b - o o - t**  !" "Really?" said the book. "A **boot** ?" The Alphablocks nodded. "Fine!" said the book. "The **woof** saw Grandma and licked his lips. He wanted to..." " **c - o o - k** !" they said. "So the **woof** went into the kitchen to **cook** dinner and they all lived happily ever after!"

The **book** closed and B and the friends all fell fast asleep.

# Bedtime!

Add lots of colour to the sleepy friends.

Moon
Baby

Onions!

Mr Onion

Sleepy
Dibillo

75

# Answers

## Pages 10-11

$2 + 1 = \boxed{3}$

$4 + 1 = \boxed{5}$

$10 - 2 = \boxed{8}$

$6 - 3 = \boxed{3}$

## Pages 14-15

## Page 26

Pup is **below** the bridge.

( above ) ( **below** )

Pup's suitcase is **open**.

( **open** ) ( closed )

Kit is standing in a **liquid**.

( **liquid** ) ( solid )

Kit's bike is **long**.

( **long** ) ( short )

## Pages 32-33

- Waffle's fur is **fluffy**.
- He has drawn **George**.
- He is **sitting** with his family.
- He got stuck **under** the fence.
- **Jelly** is in the picture.

## Pages 34-35

Duck feels like a **Happy Duck!**

## Page 43

## Pages 46-47

| j | b | b | m |
|---|---|---|---|
| a | w | u | i |
| m | n | n | l |
| e | g | g | k |

```
          d r u m
          u
          c
c   r o c k e t
a   a         e
r o b o t     d
    b
    b
    i
    t
```

## Pages 48-49

This Duggee comes next:

There are 4 red fish.

## Pages 52-53

The lynx's **fur**. The **male** lion.

## Pages 54-55

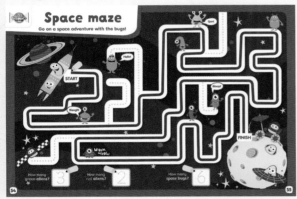

## Pages 58-59

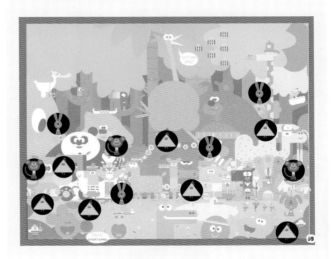

## Pages 56-57

A **stethoscope** is needed to check the heartbeat.
The rabbit weighs **2kg**.

## Pages 60-61

The Vroomster, Grimbler and Truckster are in the pictures.
There are are 4 Grimbots in total on the page.

## Pages 62-63

Airport fire engine. Ambulance.

## Pages 68-69

Seacow, lemon, Bag, bug.